The Stone In My Head

The Stone In My Head

TIM COOPER

StoryTerrace

CONTENTS

1

IT BEGAN

It started with a fall. The man who found me and called the ambulance commented to the emergency services that I'd been upright one moment, down the next. In the blink of an eye, I'd collapsed, like a thumb-push puppet when the strings go slack. I had no idea that everything was about to change.

Connaught Road in New Malden, where I fell, was the south London street on which I grew up. I'd been coming back from a day of golf, followed by dinner with friends. My wife, Kashmir, and I now lived in north London, but, My location at the time of the incident determined which hospital I was taken to and so, in the middle of the night on Saturday 27th October, I was rushed into Kingston's accident and emergency department.

Upon arrival, it was assumed I'd fallen while drunk. We'd had wine with dinner, my friends and I, but nowhere near the amount anyone would need to do what my body had done. I'd left the restaurant and was in the process of getting myself home – a full hour away – when it had happened. My memories of the hours beforehand are vague, blurry, from 10.30 p.m. that night until around 4 a.m. the following morning. Now here I was, and it was the middle of the weekend, possibly the worst time to have presented at the ER. Perhaps they thought I'd had a seizure, or had a concussion. The doctors can only diagnose what they see and – given the circumstances – I don't blame them for assuming I was a little worse for wear, that this situation was self-inflicted. It wasn't until I began to vomit dark matter that the staff – not to mention Kashmir – realised that there was something much more sinister at play. The possibility of a drunken fall was not the only misdiagnosis that would be made over the course of the next 24 hours.

So alcohol wasn't the villain. I had no memory of having tripped: my shoes weren't scuffed, my clothes weren't torn. There was little evidence to suggest that anything, really, had happened – apart from the fall.

"Did you notice anything strange that evening?" I asked my friends later down the line. "Or earlier in the day?"

"You were completely normal," they responded, their faces white with shock. "Absolutely fine."

I'd been experiencing headaches, on and off, for some time. And yet that day there hadn't been so much as a twinge. By the evening I was tired, though, and since I'd not been feeling generally well in myself of late, I was turning in at a relatively respectable hour. I'd also cut right back on booze in general. So how, exactly, had I gone from a street I knew so well, on my way home independently, to here, plugged into wires and monitors and wearing a hospital gown?

I had no idea what to think. I'd not been to the doctor about my headaches, since they're such a common complaint. There was not an ounce of me that might connect them to this moment in time.

At 1.54 a.m. the projectile vomiting began, and I was rushed through to the Majors section of the hospital. At 4 a.m. I was still waiting for the results of the CT scan, and at 6 a.m., Kashmir was advised that this would take a while, she'd not be able to see me anyway, and she might as well return home for a few hours. By the time she came back, in the bright sunlight of Sunday 28th, I'd been moved to the ACU, and a sheet of paper was waiting for her, a line of words that would form meanings that cracked our lives apart.

I have no memory of the scans, but the hospital's printed report is time-stamped 6.55am.

54-year-old male with unwitnessed fall, facial injury... LOC followed by three episodes of vomiting. Unable to recall the events.

That was all well and true. It was the next part, the CT head and facial bones scan, that hit me with the force of a tsunami.

There is a 4.2cm intra-axial hyperattenuating lesion likely to be originating in the right frontal lobe. There are also cystic lesions in the left frontal lobe measuring approximately 3.5cm. Appearances are in keeping with malignant process, likely to be a metastasis.

I remember drifting in and out of sleep, experiencing moments of lucidity and consciousness, my eyes open. And yet I was very dazed generally. My body had undergone a major event, whatever the end diagnosis might be, and I'd hurt myself considerably all over during the collapse.

The hours spent in A&E are dim, when I try to recall them. It was the ACU where things started to make a little more sense, where I began to try and piece together what on earth had just happened. And yet I have no memory of receiving the above diagnosis. In some ways, perhaps that's a blessing. There is so much else, so many clearly imprinted days, weeks and months seared into my mind, and maybe adding one more to the pile wouldn't be conducive to emotional recovery.

On Sunday, I was placed on heavy medication. This was ostensibly to keep my brain suppressed; the risk of another seizure was too high. Until they knew exactly what was going on, my brain was to be calmly controlled through sedation and steroids.

As the hours passed, I began to allow the shock of the diagnosis to seep in. There was a tumour on the brain. My brain. Tumours, not tumour. There were two. Metastasis meant cancer. It felt impossible to comprehend, too big and unwieldy to carry. To say I was frightened would be an understatement. But, as we know, in these moments of terrible shock the brain goes into protective mode. I was effectively cocooned from the worst of it for a couple of days. It just didn't feel the slightest bit real. Soon enough I'd wake up on Sunday morning, at home with my wife, and this would all have been a hideous nightmare.

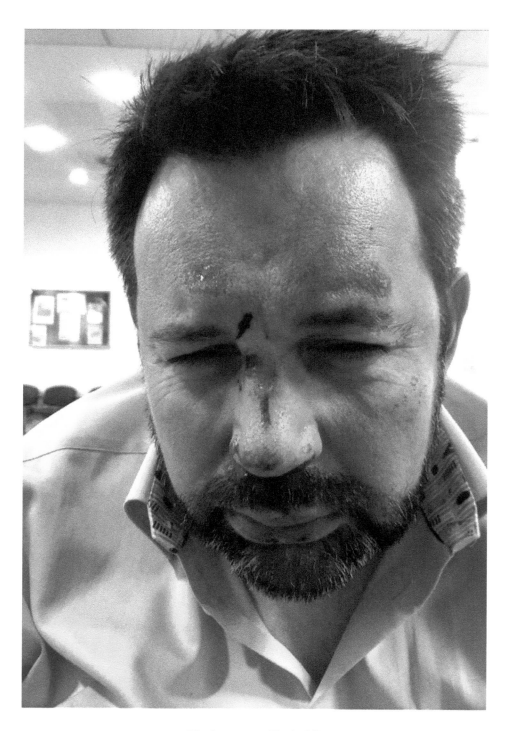

The damage caused by the fall.

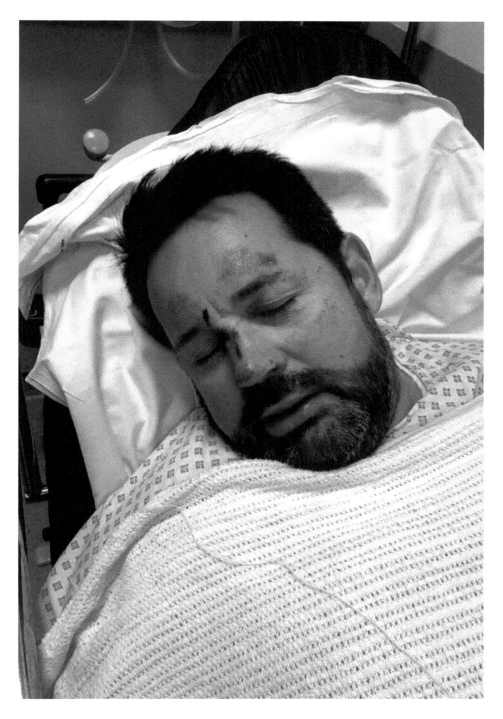

Waiting for the scans.

2

EARLY YEARS

My earliest memory is sitting in the garden eating mud. I loved to sit in our garden through the long, hot summer, amid the blooms of the roses my parents had planted – and munching on the dirt surrounding me seemed a very pleasant way to pass the time. My parents must have found it odd, but I don't remember them trying to stop me.

I was born in Kingston Hospital in 1964, and grew up in New Malden.—Many years later, as we've already seen, I was to revisit this particular hospital under very different circumstances. But we'll come to that: for now, suffice to say, I had a happy childhood.

My parents were both raised within the fashion industry, and went on to work within this sphere themselves. Both my grandfathers were named Charles, but my paternal grandfather worked in the rag trade, in manufacturing: the fur trade was enormous back then, and he was very successful within it. My maternal grandmother, Margaret, was a ladies' fashion buyer for a business called Simpsons in the Strand – based in what's now the Waterstones in Piccadilly. She worked there throughout the 1940s and 1950s, immediately following the war, and also did some modelling work. The other Charles, her husband, was a technician for the BBC. A highly educated man, he was an amazing reader, studious and serious, and he helped me a great deal with my homework as I grew up. I was lucky enough to grow up around both sets of grandparents: my mother's family came from Fulham and my father's from Clapham. It was all very local and we saw one another a great deal.

My father's parents were real party animals, and my dad went straight into the family business – C Cooper & Sons – when his father passed away, working on the fur side and on ladies' fashion. He is now 85. My mother – who passed away five years ago – was a model and had an interesting, varied career at Drummonds, the Scottish bank, until I was born.

The pair met, I think, at the local tennis club in New Malden. Our parents' lives before us are often hazy, but this much I do know: they married in 1957 and, keen to start a family, were forced to wait at least five years for my arrival. Unfortunately, their second pregnancy – when I was six years older – did not survive and my mother suffered a miscarriage. It would have been much more traumatic for her than for anyone else, I believe: before my birth she had been praying for a child, and I think they were both keen to have more. But I was shielded from the loss and there was no part of me, growing up, that longed for a sibling. My mother herself was an only child, and in a way that shared experience made us closer.

My father's sister, however, had three children – the eldest three years younger than me, the youngest eight. I was therefore leader of the pack, and since they were local – just round the corner in Raynes Park – we were one unit, one shared family.

I was lucky enough to be sent to a private primary school, and had some very happy times at The Study, in New Malden. I can remember my pride on the first day, standing there in my deep scarlet blazer, my black and gold tie and new shorts. I've always loved learning, and enjoyed my time at primary school very much: "enthusiastic" best describes myself at that age. At the age of 10, I moved schools to Ewell Castle, in Ewell near Epsom: it took boarders and day boys, and I fell into the latter category.

My parents always encouraged learning, and my maternal grandparents would often pick me up from school and help me with my assignments back at their house. I adored maths and was always very interested in acquiring knowledge on that front; everything else seemed to pale into insignificance beside the wonderful rules and formulae associated with numbers. Once the other subjects' prep was out of the way, eventually my mother and I would return home, and later on my father would join us.

Without doubt, my mother was the more present parent:

I loved, and still love my father dearly, but he worked incredibly long hours during my childhood and adolescence, and so appeared more distant to me. It was golf, in fact, that took up the majority of his time. He was selected to be on the squad for the Walker Cup, and had been a member of his local county team since long before I was born. He was excellent, played for Surrey and was hugely respected in the golfing community. Throughout my childhood, he was often on the links both Saturday and Sunday, though later on he dropped the Saturday sessions. As I grew older, I joined him on these weekends: my mother played too, and she taught me. It wasn't until I was around 11 that I realised the strength required and, with lessons, began to really enjoy myself.

I can say with honesty that I took up the sport to become closer to my father, and indeed it's what I'd been doing on the day that changed my life forever. I could have no idea of this, as a little boy, but the discipline and mental strength the game teaches were to stand me in very good stead. The game of golf is one played primarily against oneself: it's a challenge, one of mind and character. Of course, you compete against others, but when it comes down to it, what matters is your aim, your eye, your shot. A battle against oneself. How grimly ironic that early life lesson was eventually to become.

Captain Scarlett, my favourite childhood TV series!

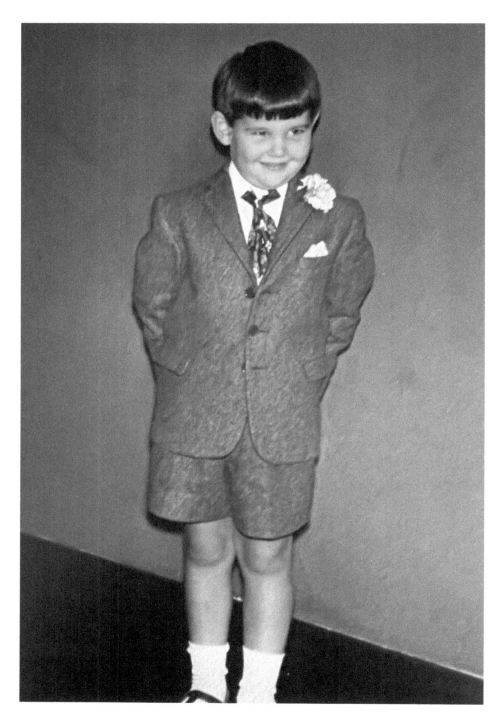

Well dressed boy.

3

SCHOOL DAYS

'm grateful for the atmosphere of energy and fun within which I grew up. With my parents and grandparents, life was always a party, and as I grew older this became increasingly useful. I could mingle with the adults, chat and listen in on conversations I didn't quite understand – it was all such an education. I'd hear the music someone had put on at midnight and wander over to the record player to take a look. Whenever my parents and their friends had been out somewhere, it was back to our house they always came for the after-party. My mum had sausage rolls ready to heat up, and my dad would begin carrying out bottles of whiskey and wine. Over time, when someone asked for music, I began to volunteer. Soon I wasn't just sneaking down, hoping not to be caught: I was actively participating. There was nothing better than watching them all rush onto the dance floor. And as word got out about my blossoming DJ skills, more senior members of the golf club might ask me to handle the music at the club's major events. I can remember one do, a dinner-dance, and my absolute beaming pride in the gorgeous royal-blue dinner suit my uncle had handed down to me. I was all ruffled shirt and bow tie, ready to step up to the decks.

It emerged as a huge passion, music. I spent every penny of pocket money or cash earned from odd jobs on my records, and was amassing quite the collection. I was particularly interested in soul, in Motown and Michael Jackson, R&B, The Supremes. The whole genre and its individual players has long fascinated me. But DJing isn't about playing simply what you enjoy – and luckily I had a wide taste. From the ages of 15 to 22 I would set up my cassette recordings or vinyl for friends' 18th birthdays, 21st parties and the like. And I learned the guitar at school, too, so was playing myself: I kept up with it until I started work at the age of 18, in fact.

I can remember playing on the school's football and cricket team, depending on the season, but when I left full-time education, I concentrated on golf. I was an active participant, though, and enjoyed the sports I was introduced to. Inside the classroom was another matter. Unfortunately, my maternal grandfather died in the early part of 1981, at precisely the time my peers were beginning the long months of revision for their O levels. I had been told by Ewell Castle that my capabilities were high, but when it came to those exams I didn't fulfil them, and instead did a very good job of failing them. It's no excuse, grief, but it does help to explain some of my inability to concentrate, to do the work necessary for success. And yet I'd sat my maths O level a year in advance, and passed with flying colours. It just goes to show that under different circumstances I could have performed better, perhaps.

By the time I was 13, my parents had begun to teach me the basic skills of accounting, and soon enough I was writing up the ledgers, completing the balancing of books manually. It was all part and parcel of the family business, something I knew my father wanted me to continue in his name, when the time was right.

I'd been awarded a good-enough grade in physics and art, but needed to retake my English O level – my parents and I both agreed this was a necessity. At Nescot (North East Surrey College of Technology) I took computer studies, photography and English. By the time these were completed and I'd got the grades, I was ready to leave education and create something for myself, and so it was that I found myself a job in an accounting department as a purchase-ledger clerk at Gulliver's Travel Agency, a global tour operator. I was delighted to be putting my numerical skills to good use, and thrived in the world of work.

I knew my father was disappointed about my lack of willingness to join the family firm, but honestly, having managed the books for several years on my own, I couldn't see how the business could afford two incomes. There wouldn't be enough for me to draw the level of salary I envisaged for myself, the level that would make me feel financially secure. I'd watched my father work either five or six full, busy days a week for most of my life; economic shifts and changes were only making life more challenging for him, and the company's income was in decline. It would have been the wrong decision for me to join C Cooper & Son, and I have no regrets about not doing so. Nonetheless, I remained involved, not costing the company a penny, and took on a directorship with certain responsibilities.

I'd finished with school and was keen to forge my own path, use the knowledge and education and passion I did have to better my own situation. I earnt £4,000 a year, and by the time I turned 19, I'd spent a year in the world of work and bought myself a flat in Surbiton. One of my aunties had left me some money when she died, not to be used until I was 18 – thank heavens, or I'd have spent it on records – and I managed to get a £20,000 mortgage with a £5,000 deposit.

I don't honestly believe I'd do anything differently, if I met myself at that age, and could impart some advice. I knew my strengths and weaknesses and I was determined to play to the former. Working and earning were important to me: education was one thing, but it didn't just come in textbooks and academic study. I highly doubt university would have given me much besides three years of fun. And I could have that perfectly well on my own terms. I'd been raised with the example of my father, who did everything he could to provide for us all. I wanted to be like him, to play golf and listen to my music and leave the house each morning with a sense of direction. By the time I finished college, I was ready to do just that. And I was a homeowner before I was 20. It felt like things were falling spectacularly into place.

The young football player!

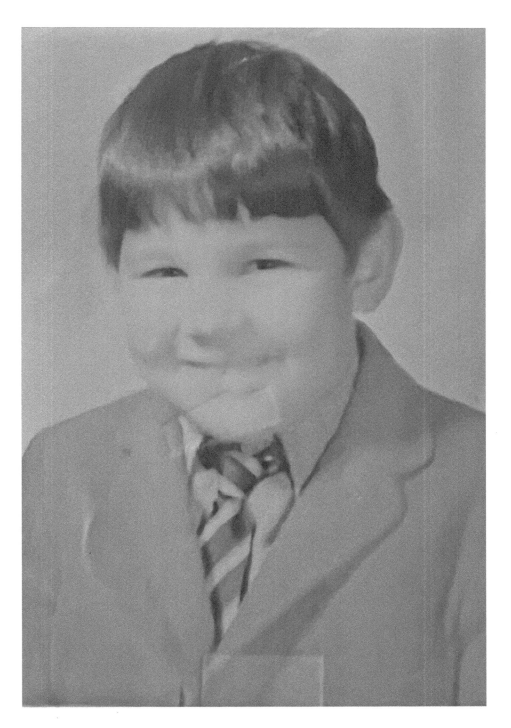

Primary school.

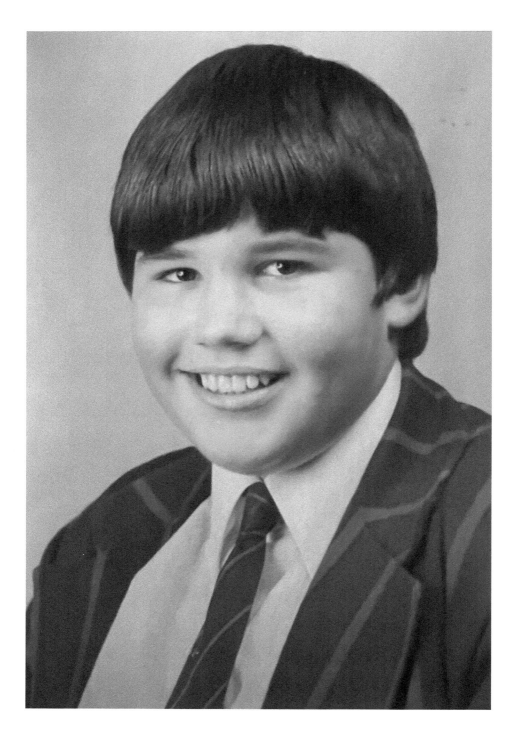

Secondary school.

Teenage DJ!

4

WORKING NINE TO FIVE

There will be times in everybody's life when the ability to work – to earn and provide – is compromised. The past year has taught us all this lesson many times over, and the knock-on effects will be felt for many years to come. But my own taste of a professional life put on hold through necessity came long before our recent, collective experience. It made me reflect on the importance of work in my own life, and just how grateful I am for the joy my career has given me.

Work is about success, but this comes in a number of guises. It's about personal satisfaction as well as a financial reward. I'm not mercenary, but I enjoy a good life and see part of my success and enterprise in the decent financial returns I've produced. There is also that sense of pride in appreciation, either from a team or a client. I felt such a sense of purpose throughout my working life, and continue to feel this today. I appreciate good leaders and enjoyed being seen as one. I loved being creative: drawing up solutions to problems and then implementing them. 'Integrity' is a huge word in my vocabulary, though, and an important part of my make-up. Everything must be done for the right reasons.

I worked from the age of 18 right up until my diagnosis. Following my first job at Gulliver's, I worked within the sphere of management consultancy as a finance assistant and worked my way up to become the financial controller for Touche Ross Management Consultancy. Early in my career, through my involvement in the tourism and leisure sectors, I was able to combine my personal life and passions alongside work. Eventually, I realised that I wanted to understand other environments, businesses and industries, but I'd had my eyes opened to the excitement of management consultancy. In November 1989, I joined Interbrand, a very large creative-design consultancy which specialised in brand naming. I assisted the chairman, chief executive and group finance director with corporate brand strategy, and my accounting skills came into play too during brand valuations. I worked on sales and marketing plans, business plans, and absolutely loved the creativity of it all working across seven territories.

I was made redundant when the company moved the executive team to New York following an acquisition with a larger business. But I was young enough and the experience wasn't wasted – I can remember going in to meet my boss and asking whether the envelope in his hand was a plane ticket or a letter. There were no hard feelings when it turned out to be the latter, and I landed a new role at a company called Marketing by Design.

The business had got off to a flying start, but they didn't have an accountant in-house, and I was brought in as de facto general manager. I ran up the numbers and gave them the bad news – but also the strategy. We worked with some huge consumer brands, from Unilever and P&G to Mars Confectionery, Kraft Foods and Sharwood's. We delivered the idea of the Mars ice-cream and the concept of 'fun-size' bars, as well as the redesign of the packaging. It felt great: our little business in Wimbledon was flying high. And then, another sling and arrow of outrageous fortune, the 1991-92 recession hit and our largest client – Proctor & Gamble – cut its marketing budget by 90%. This put us into liquidation, but the majority shareholder and I were the last two employees left, and we managed the closing and collapsing of the company without burning too many bridges, as can sometimes happen. I think what these experiences gave me was a strong resolve and a backbone. You can work as hard as you like, but you cannot control outside forces. Sometimes fate takes over. A useful lesson for later on in my life, as we shall see, but also a door opening on new opportunities.

In July 1992, I became self-employed and founded The Cooper Consultancy. I'd built up my contacts and my confidence over many years, and felt excited by the next stage. The headline of my new company was simply: I'd help companies to make more profit. I continued successfully for three years until an offer of employment came through from a previous client, Crown Business Communications, and I joined their executive team from 1995 to 2001. Over the course of these years, the company's staff increased from 20 to 140 and saw growth from £1m turnover to £15m. I was awarded an equity stake in 1998 and a directorship in 1999.

When Crown was sold, I decided to take a career break. I've enjoyed a couple of the things throughout the span of my career, and would do so again in a heartbeat – on my own terms, of course. This one meant that, from 2001 to 2003, I was able to oversee the construction of my own house in West Sussex.

From here, I embarked on a series of directorships and strategic-consultancy roles and by January 2007 I was involved in the management buyout of a call-centre business, and set up Happy People Group, which became a multi-million-pound marketing service group. Here, I was responsible for its overall business management, strategy and direction. Between January 2014 and June 2016, I took another sabbatical, touring the world and experiencing new cultures – and Kashmir and I were married. By 2016, I'd set up my own wine and accessory retail business online, followed by an art branch in 2017.

It had been a hugely satisfying career, filled with enough time both for myself and wherever I was working. I felt the balance was just right, and whenever the scales tipped too far on one side or the other, I corrected them. I was financially secure, had an excellent track record, and had overseen many successful mergers, acquisitions and branding initiatives. I was at the top of my game and loving life.

Office photo.

Work event.

Speaker event.

5

A GATHERING STORM

Despite the fulfilling nature of my career, my recent wedding and the general contentedness I felt, it seemed – between around 2013 and 2015 – that my behaviour was changing. Over the course of a few months in 2016 I was becoming frustrated, finding personal and professional relationships a struggle and my capabilities suddenly changed. I was simply not the man I once was. And I couldn't understand why.

"Did you manage to call the plumber today?" Kashmir would ask, as we sat down for dinner.

I'd stare at her, confused. She *had* asked me to do that and I'd completely forgotten.

"It slipped my mind," I'd say. Kashmir's job was – and is – international. She works in tech for large corporates, amongst other things. She didn't have the time for this. I said I'd pull my weight and it wasn't happening.

"Slipping your mind isn't an excuse," she'd say, sadly. The conversation would move on, but I could sense her frustration. This dynamic would play out time and again, and I had no idea what was happening to me. Was this just what it meant to grow older, to become a little more slapdash, a little less organised? No one had told me that one's whole personality would undergo such a shift. What on earth was going on? And why was my work not filling me with the sense of drive and purpose it once had?

The fact was, I simply wasn't as switched on as I'd once been. I felt sluggish, tired, forgetful, and this transformation from how I had once been caused friction between Kashmir and me. The resulting feelings of disappointment where causing me a lot of stress. I had no idea what was causing the problem, and so – as might be expected – I felt more and more useless, and beat myself up. On reflection, during those years as the storm clouds gathered, I wouldn't honestly have felt confident expressing myself to the plumber, even if I'd remembered to call them. My cognitive functions seemed to be less than they once were. Above all, it was frightening.

And now I had the growing trend of headaches to be dealing with. They began in the summer of 2015, and were growing more severe by the month. At first I managed the pain with paracetamol, but over time this became unsustainable: the pain was too great. And yet I didn't go to the doctor: how common are headaches, after all? I simply felt I had to buck up my ideas, reclaim my old drive and impetus, and work on improving the quality of my thinking.

I believed that, with a little dedication, I could beat the physical manifestations of worry.

Soon enough, though, when the paracetamol barely touched the sides of the pain, I'd sleep the headaches off. This in turn made me more sluggish, more desperate. I can remember one occasion when I had to really control myself while driving – I felt frightened, disoriented and in great danger. Somehow I got myself back home and went straight to bed. Often these enforced sleeps would last three hours, and gradually – as one does – I seemed to learn to live with it, simply accept it as part and parcel of who I was now. I became almost tolerant to the pain.

Looking back, they weren't traditional headaches by any means: the pain was firmly lodged in the back of my skull. I know now that the tumour I was soon to discover grew, essentially, from fluids in my brain. There are four reserves called ventricles containing this fluid, which keeps the spine moving, and later my surgeon would describe my condition as "being like a cold in the brain". It was like a virus had grown in the fluid, causing "dirty water" (how I described it) the tumour to take its form. And it was growing in the exact space required by my brain for executive function. Later, Kashmir and I would sit listening to the surgeon, nodding our heads as he asked about pain, about foggy thoughts, about a lack of drive. I could see Kashmir's guilt writ large on her face – but neither of us could apologise for something we didn't know about. It did help to explain a great deal, of course.

I'd been worrying about the loss of a sense of purpose for months, by this point – for years even. I wanted to get on and do something, contribute to the world somehow, and yet I couldn't see how. If 28th October had never happened, who knows how long I might have continued in this way. I'm a private person by nature, sometimes quite insular: I suppose, in many ways, when it comes to personal problems, my only-child syndrome kicks in, and I rail against needing to depend on other people. I'd forged my own career, been independent and travelled widely. I didn't want to admit weakness, to express what was going on within.

I was no stranger to health problems, though. At the age of 29 I'd been diagnosed with the possibility, later on, of glaucoma – a hereditary disease on my father's side of the family. I had been conscious of my health from then on: mindful of what I ate and drank, and determined not to succumb to high blood-pressure as a result of work, or diet, or lifestyle. I'm by no means obsessive, and have never been one to turn down a treat if it's offered – that's no way to live. But I watched my weight carefully and was keen to remain in shape. And yet I went to the doctor only when it was absolutely necessary, and only when things had become bad in one way or the other. I felt, honestly, that I could handle whatever life threw at me.

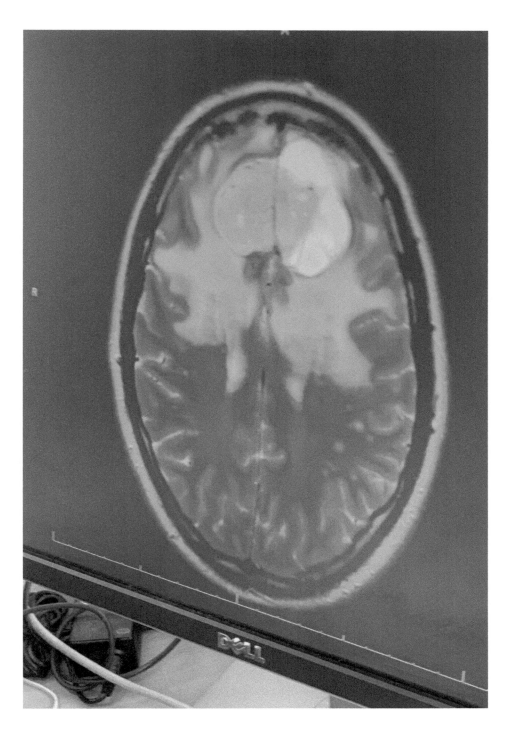

The two tumours joined together!

6

SAVIOURS

I lay in bed staring at the sheet in front of me. The early hours of 29th October 2018 are something of a blur, but I can remember the distinct feeling of dread that settled on my chest. I had not one but two tumours. I'd collapsed. There was a clinical doctor's diagnosis in front of me filled with jargon, with words I couldn't comprehend then but which would become grimly familiar. There was no time for a bedside manner then. I was to speak to specialists, but who knew when?

I stayed at Kingston Hospital from the Sunday through to the Thursday, with a referral booked at St George's in Tooting for the following Friday. For over a week, Kashmir and I were facing down the long barrel of uncertainty. We didn't know whether my tumours were cancerous – though the diagnosis sheet seemed to think so – or whether, if it was cancer, it was primary or secondary.

I had to wait: to be a patient patient. I had the MRI on Wednesday and was discharged the following day, not a moment too soon. I was on a bizarre ward when I first left the ACU, surrounded by middle-aged men with a variety of different problems, and most of them quite cantankerous. It revealed to me, as nothing else ever had, just how desperate some people's situations truly were. One of the men, a particularly big guy, had severe depression as a part of his bipolar disorder, and suicidal tendencies: the staff seemed to know him well and he'd been in and out of hospital many times, both for mental-health and physical issues.

I can remember waking up in the middle of the night, as Tuesday ticked over into the day of the MRI; I'd felt a drop of water on my face and there he was, standing above me, inches from my face and sweating onto me. His condition was very poor, and it was clear he needed to be in a psychiatric facility: on another evening he urinated into another patient's locker. There was an absolute uproar when the gentleman in question – the eldest on our ward – discovered this.

By the time I was discharged, I'd truly had enough. Five days in hospital was easily the longest I'd ever spent in such a place, and the sense of claustrophobia and airlessness was only amplified by my fear of what the next week might bring. Just five days before, I'd been living my life, enjoying a sunny day on the links, and now this. The food on the ward was appalling, full of rubbish and sugar, and I couldn't shake the thought from my mind that such a poor diet was likely to increase my chances of a tougher battle with cancer.

The nurses were so disappointed that I wouldn't eat, but it seemed counter-intuitive to do so.

On the Friday, safely back at home, we received a phone call from one of the nurses at St George's. My case had been reviewed in the regular Friday morning meeting, when all the teams come together to discuss various patients and their problems. I was informed that the specialist had confirmed my condition was most likely to be a meningioma. These are tumours that form on the membranes covering the brain and spinal cord, just inside the skull, on the meninges.

The nurse relaying the news to me sounded bright and buoyant. "It's good news," she assured me. "Most meningiomas aren't cancerous. You're very lucky."

I felt anything but. As I've found out since, my condition was still very serious, and cancer or not, there remained something in my head that I didn't want there. It had caused me to collapse in the middle of the street. I appreciated that the scale of the news might be better than the initial diagnosis, but the team still needed to find out for sure. The only way to do that was through a biopsy – they could have no concrete proof of the tumour's benign nature until they examined the tissue. And if it was cancerous, was it a primary or secondary cancer?

I suppose, looking back, that I was still in such complete and utter shock that my mind accepted the next steps. I was gamma tested, or so I called it, using radioactive injections designed to reveal the presence of cancer in the rest of the body. I received the dreaded results: there was no cancer in the rest of my body. I can remember that huge relief. And that did help me accept the consultants' reassurance that things, now, were not as bad as they could be.

The following Wednesday, 7th November, Kashmir and I went to meet with my consultant surgeon, Mr Simon Stapleton. He was a reassuring man – practical, dedicated and calm. He explained everything to me, discussed my options, and showed me the MRI results. The questions he asked, and the answers we gave, helped me piece together the slow progression of events and tell-tale signs that had led to this moment.

I was booked in for an operation on 20th November, less than a month after that dreadful day when everything changed. I now had a fortnight of fear to contend with – what had happened on 28th October had shaken me badly, but I'd had no time to process it. I was terrified I might fall asleep and never wake again, like an appliance with its battery suddenly removed. One moment I'd been there, walking down this oh-so-familiar road, and the next I'd been on the floor. Whatever was inside my head needed to come out. I couldn't endure another collapse, another loss of memory, another period of hospitals and tests and constant monitoring. There was an intruder here, and it was about to be evicted.

7

THE OPERATION

I had no idea whether or not the operation would prove to be a success; I could only hope. I had follow-up appointments after the initial consultation with Mr Stapleton, and otherwise tried to keep myself as occupied as possible before the operation. I couldn't go over it or under it: I had to force myself through it.

We were asked to present at the hospital the night before my scheduled surgery, and arrived at 7 p.m. on 19th November. By some miracle, I was shown to a private room at St George's, and Kashmir, my mother-in-law and our friend Vanessa helped settled me in. By 8.30 I'd been checked in, just like at a hotel, and then the doctor arrived to fit my cannula. This seemed to be the cue for everyone bar Kashmir to leave, and I noticed – as they did so – that they had tears in their eyes. I knew what this emotion meant. There was a chance, however slim, that I wouldn't make it through this operation.

Having the cannula inserted was painful, but I was

touched when the doctor advised me he would be on the surgical team the next morning. "I'll be there in the operating theatre with you," he said, and I felt myself tear up immediately.

"I'm so grateful to meet you," I said. He came back to see me some days after the operation, to check in and see how I was getting on. The staff, I came to realise quickly, were always busy but they were never too busy. Every single doctor, nurse or surgeon I encountered was incredible, dedicated and kind. I felt a well of affection once again for the amazing NHS and what they were doing for me. It must take an awful lot of mental strength, I thought that night, to work somewhere like this, surrounded by injuries and diagnoses, decisions and moments of final, terrifying stillness.

In the moment, of course, the doctors and nurses and consultants take charge. They need you to be ready. My wife took my personal effects away, and I was left with a bag of overnight clothes, my washbag and my medication. She kissed me goodbye and repeated the criteria we'd decided on together: "I want you to wake up," she said, "recognise me, and tell me you love me." I nodded through my tears, and she was gone.

I had a promise to keep and was determined not to let her down. But as I lay there in that lonely room, I prepared myself mentally for the possibility of a negative outcome. What if a mistake was made? What if something went wrong, and I was left without the power of speech, movement, reasoning, memory? What if I was a different person altogether? I've never been so frightened in my life. I'd done whatever research I was bold enough to do, and my mind wandered to the images I'd seen: to the blood and gore, to the fact my head would soon be opened up and peeled back, my face lifted forward. My imagination ran wild. There would be no nips and tucks here: the job was simply to remove the tumours. I wept in my private room, both sad and glad that there was no one there around me. Perhaps, I reasoned, this would be my last night on Earth: no amount of reassurance from friends, family or medical professionals could have reassured me.

My operation was at 10.30 a.m. the following morning, and I had a final call with Kashmir just beforehand. Finally it was time to go. I wondered what exactly I needed to bring with me, and was assured by the anaesthetist's team that all was well. They put me at ease, or tried to, asking me about myself, my hobbies, my life.

"Please be careful with these," I said, taking off my glasses at last. "I need them." Without them I wouldn't be able to see a thing; I'd had to wear them since I was 12. It was a moment of light-hearted humour, a moment more of the life that had come before. And then, as I lay down in the theatre, it was time to begin. All I needed to do, I reasoned, was go to sleep and wake back up again. Whatever happened in here I would deal with it. I would endeavour with every fibre of my being to pull through. Optimism was all I had.

"Countdown from 10, please," I was told. I got to eight, and it all went black.

It was the second time in my life I'd had a general anaesthetic: an incredible, masterful invention when one considers what it does. After seven hours under its spell, at 5.30 p.m., the operation was finished and my body, slowly and groggily, began to wake up from its enforced slumber. The first thing I remember was a feeling, and that feeling was pain. Immense pain, more pain than I'd ever felt. I was far too nervous to move, but slowly – ever so slowly – I opened my eyes.

I was on the ACU, where two nurses were now in charge of my care. I'd been in the recovery room prior to this, post-operation, and was now one rung down from intensive care. It was as they moved me that I slowly began to regain consciousness.

Kashmir was there, waiting. I saw her, and shakily – I could speak! – told her I loved her. The criteria had been met.

As Kashmir was talking to me, my face suddenly became lopsided and swollen, and my speech began to slur.

"Something's not right!" Kashmir shouted, running for the nurses. "Come quick – look at his face!"

Panic ensued. I had been fitted with a tube at the back of my head which was designed to drain away the blood and fluid caused by the surgery. Kashmir was asked to leave and waited outside while the two specialist nurses assigned to me pulled the curtains shut. The drain had become blocked somehow and fluid was filling my face. They prepared to rush me for an MRI X-ray, but miraculously, as they moved me, something happened to disturb the blockage and by the time I arrived at the scan, it was clear once more.

I was given so much incredible care by these nurses, and yet nothing can prepare you for the trauma of preparing for surgery and its immediate aftermath. In those moments – as I watched Kashmir's smile fall away, heard the screech of the curtain pull, the concern of the nurses and later, as I was injected with morphine to tame the pain – I was gripped by horror, by feelings of despair. How on earth had it come to this? And had the surgery designed to save my life actually worked? At this stage I had no idea.

The tests – cognitive function, speech, reasoning – would all come later. For now, all I could really focus on was the here and now: I was alive, and in this moment experiencing too much agony to be aware of much else. Whatever came next would come. For now I needed to sleep.

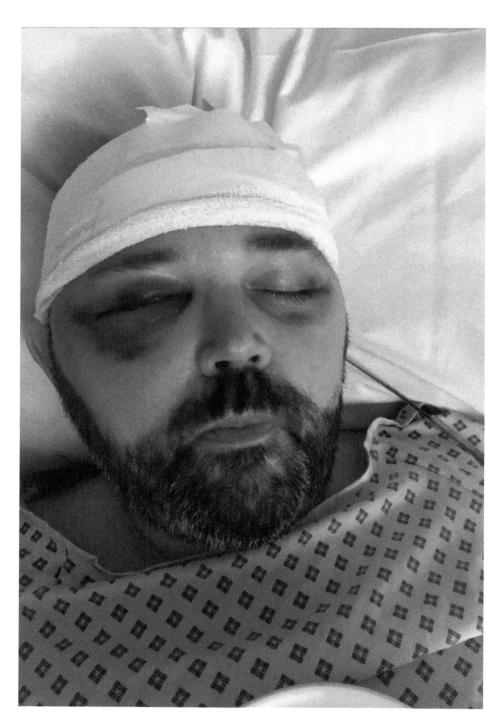

The day after surgery, 21st November 2018.

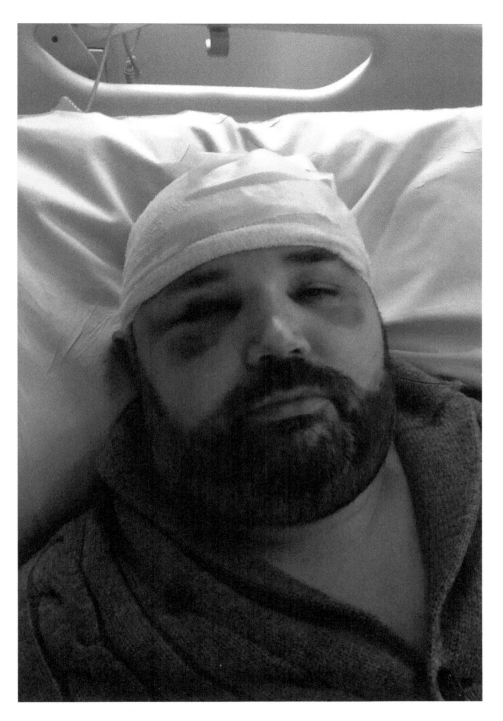

Second day after surgery, 22nd November 2018.

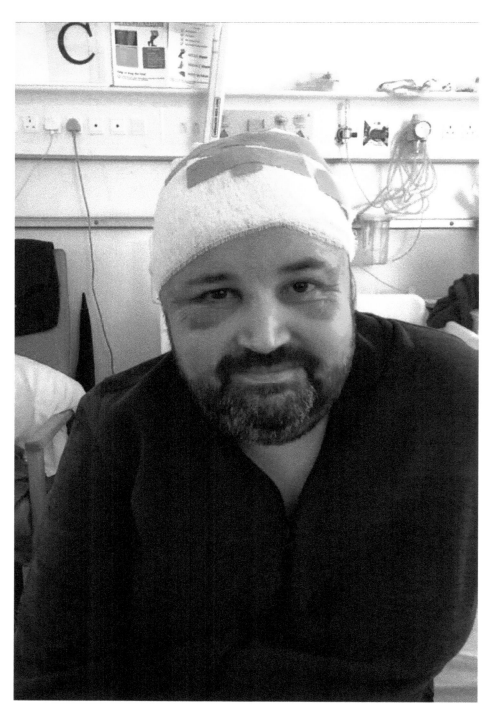

Sitting up for the first time since the operation, 23rd November 2018.

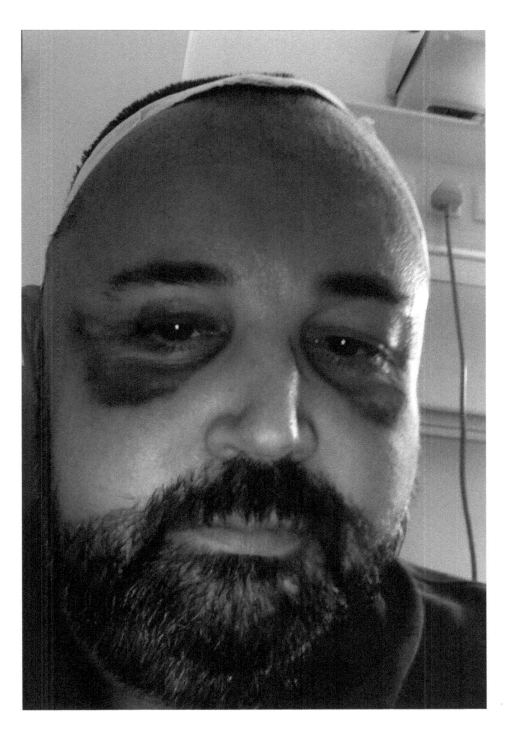

The big head bandage is removed, 25th November 2018.

My scar line after the painful removal of the clips that were holding my head together,
27th November 2018.

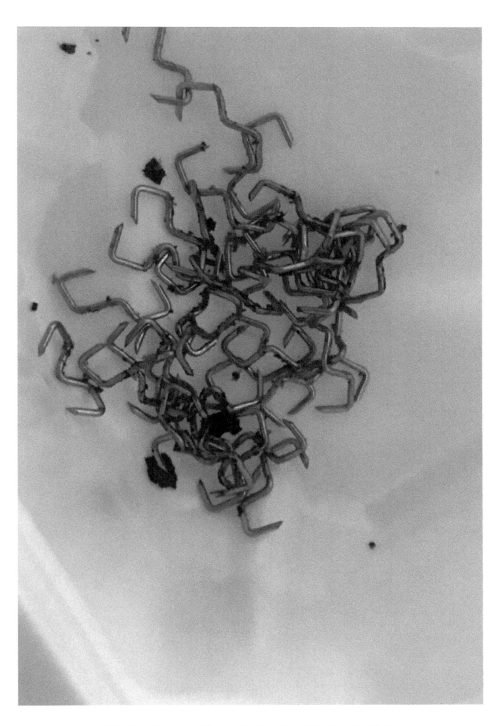

The clips that were holding my head together, 27th November 2018.

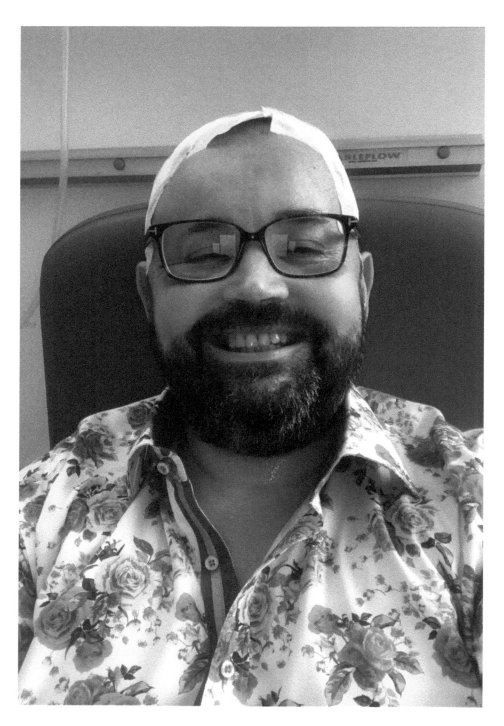

Smiling on discharge day, 29th November 2018.

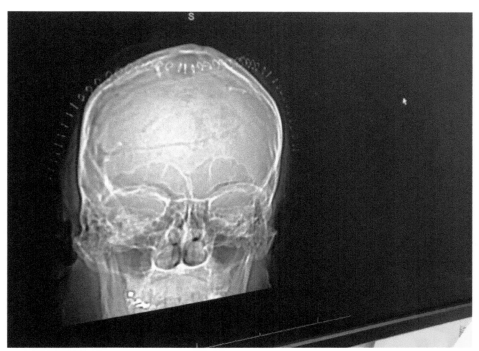

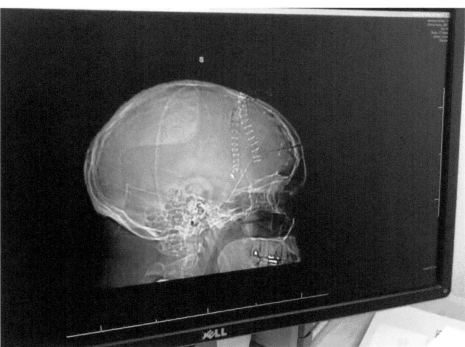

Post operation MRI.

8

AFTERMATH

"Is there any news?" As soon as I felt mentally able to ask the question, I did. The nurse smiled at me.

"We can't tell you," she said gently, "but the doctor will come and see you soon."

She must have seen the look on my face. "We've been instructed that it's gone well, though," she added.

There was no way of me assessing just how well things had gone, of course, and I knew that my brain would not survive a second operation. It had to have gone well. Everything rested on that. I felt relief mingled with the fear: I'd just heard the nurse tell me it was a success, hadn't I? Or had there been complications? What was the exact standard of "going well"? I also knew, at this point, that until a biopsy had been completed on the tumour, there was no way of knowing if it had indeed been cancerous or not.

In addition, that first day was spent testing the limits of what felt like a new body. I was nervous of any form of movement, and in the end allowed my body to do what it clearly wanted to, and rest. This, I supposed, in my morphine-befuddled state, was a healing process in itself.

Hospitals truly are incredible places. In my drugged, frightened but exhilarated state I lay back and let the noise overtake me: the bleeping machines, the footsteps on linoleum, the wheels of a trolley. It was a busy place, and an unnerving environment. My response to this was to remain as quiet as possible, try to surround myself with an oasis of calm and wait for the next day. There was literally nothing else to be done. I was heavily bandaged and had two huge black eyes; my face was swollen. I knew this next phase was important for my long-term recovery – I had to be a good boy, not move too much, take it all in my stride, and do as the nurses instructed. One realises very quickly how hospitals are just like a machine, well-oiled and put to excellent use, and how quickly one must adapt to being a cog within it. I couldn't walk to the bathroom on my own, so had to relinquish my pride and submit to bed-baths and bed-pans. I can see the humour in it now, and am grateful that the anaesthetic, combined with other drugs I'd been put on, causes constipation. In short, I had to surrender to the expert knowledge of those looking after me. Miraculously, on Monday I was moved to my own room.

I spent three full days in this way, and on the Saturday was allowed out of bed for the first time. It was a bizarre feeling, suddenly standing up, realising I could walk – albeit slowly – and experiencing that strange sensation of strength (I'd survived) combined with weakness (my body protesting at the trauma I'd put it through). That day, I was moved to a more general ward, as opposed to the post-surgery, intensive care unit or the ACU, and was allowed some visitors in the days that followed. I was also permitted, after some rendezvous trips with a male nurse, to have an unassisted shower. By the Tuesday I was able to get about on my own – just a week after such major surgery.

The biopsy results took five days to arrive, and it was on the Monday that Mr Stapleton came to visit. I'd met a lot of his team in the days in between – his was such a highly pressurised team, full of registrars and senior doctors – but now he was here himself to deliver the news.

"So, Tim, how've you been?" he asked.

"I'm making progress, I think." And it was true. I felt a little better each day.

"I have the results of the biopsy here."

I nodded. This was why he'd come personally. He didn't draw the moment out or add to the tension, but the mere seconds between his two statements – I have the results, and here they are – seemed to stretch into hours. I could feel every fibre of myself coil up, the adrenaline preparing to course through my system. I would fight whatever this was every step of the way: now I just needed to know exactly who the enemy was.

"It's benign, Tim."

I stared at him, trying to read his expression. I was almost certain this was a good thing, but the after-effects of surgery, medication and weeks of mental exhaustion had taken their toll.

"Ok," I said evenly. "And that means… non-cancerous?"

"Yes, non-cancerous. It'll be a long road, but you've made it through."

I was speechless, momentarily stunned. Mr Stapleton continued:

"The extraction was a clean job."

"So," I said, struggling to speak, "exactly how much of my brain did you take away?"

He smiled, surprised. "No one's ever asked me that before," he chuckled. "It's not something we measure, unfortunately."

"But surely there must have been parts that came away – parts of the brain that came away with the tumour?"

"Well, yes," he said, "It was a mucous membrane we were excising. But whatever was extracted in terms of the brain itself will grow back – the tissue recovers."

He went on to tell me about the importance of regaining my cognitive functions, and explained about the occupational therapy team who would guide me through the process.

It was an emotional meeting, of course, but the real relief came later – once Mr Stapleton had gone, once I was on my own, once I had time to reflect. I didn't have brain cancer. I didn't have a primary cancer lurking elsewhere in my body. And the growth that had caused my terrifying loss of consciousness on 28th October was no more. It was not a part of my body any longer. The moment that tube was removed from the back of my head was sheer euphoria: it had been stitched, essentially sewn into my scalp with thread and glue. Makes you realise how, despite our amazing advances in Western medicine, sometimes the measures taken to patch someone together are pretty barbaric.

I was now faced with the brain-function tests required to assess me. These were a huge challenge and I dreaded the brainteasers, the numeric questions, the reading and writing and copying signs made by the nurses. The tests were marked out of 30, and in my first attempt I scored 16 – this was concerning. The assessments continued every day, alongside physiotherapy sessions that were more concerned with neurological function. I was hardly running around but on this front, things were fine. I was able to push back against the nurses' hands with my palms or feet; my peripheral vision and eye coordination all seemed to be in order. My blood and oxygen levels were constantly monitored during this time, as well as blood pressure and blood sugar – the risk of secondary infections after an operation as traumatic as mine was high, as was the possibility of blood clotting. I'd not moved for three solid days after the surgery, after all. My vitals were monitored constantly, and for the first two nights after the operation I wore a belt across my chest to ensure my heart was functioning exactly as it should. There was every likelihood I could have a seizure.

It doesn't sound like the rosiest picture, does it? And yet, in the end, I remained in hospital for a mere eight days following the surgery. On Wednesday 28th November – a month to the day since I'd collapsed in Connaught Road – I was informed I'd be able to return home on the Friday: a real bonus, since this happened also to be Kashmir's birthday. When it came down to it, though, Mr Stapleton came to see me on the 29th to let me know I was likely well enough to go home that day. There was extreme pressure on the staff in terms of bed space, and it was felt that I was not being put at risk leaving a day earlier than planned.

I called Kashmir to tell her the good news, and soon enough the wheels were in motion: I was to leave in the mid-afternoon. The nurses began the process of requesting my medication from the pharmacy, and soon enough I had my discharge papers. The nurse ran through the medication timetable with Kashmir and handed over my paperwork, and within no time at all we were heading home in the car. The fresh air was exhilarating: I'd not had a breath of it for so long, and felt instantly lightheaded. We now needed to navigate the busy London streets all the way from Tooting to Camden along the bumpy roads, Kashmir nervously glancing over at me as I winced for each of the potholes.

My mother-in-law and two-year-old niece were living with us at the time, which would have been a help to Kashmir in the early days, and was certainly a help to me once I'd taken the time to rest. For the days that followed my discharge,

I was managing to be up and about for around an hour a day, no more. I hadn't even begun to process what had happened to me; I simply didn't have the mental energy.

What I do remember as being especially difficult, in those early days, was my desire to prove I was capable. Whilst still in hospital, I'd had to prove to the occupational therapy team that I could make food for myself: scrambled eggs on toast, a cup of tea. If I'd been living alone at the time, I'd have been assigned a carer to assist with such everyday tasks, but the fact I'd managed to complete them made me bolder. I wanted to make my own breakfast, progress as quickly as possible, put it all behind us. As the weeks drew on, the biggest challenge became my mental state.

I was on steroids to reduce inflammation for several days after leaving hospital, and was still thoroughly bandaged. What I realise, looking back at the pictures, was just how far there was to go. Mr Stapleton had advised me of the long road to recovery, but it felt like too much to contend with at that stage. Now, on top of everything else that had happened, I had to be patient again?

We lived in Camden, and therefore the north London teams who'd been informed of my surgery sent nurses to help with the cleaning of my scar. I wanted to be able to do it myself, and I know Kashmir felt the same. I knew I wasn't right yet, and that there was a long way to go. I couldn't sit back and take the help, though. For the first time in my life I exhibited a temper, feeling frustrated and anxious and worrying about how on earth I was to put my life back together. My tumour was gone, but what should I do now? There was no handbook, no step-by-step guide.

Christmas was a helpful distraction, of course, and I so enjoyed the time spent with my family. My niece especially was a joy: it's impossible to be gloomy with a toddler wandering around, singing and playing without a care in the world. Kashmir had explained to her that I had "a stone" in my head that the doctors had removed in the hospital. I can still remember so vividly the moment when I returned home, grateful to be alive but so exhausted, with my niece smiling up at me.

"How's the stone in your head, Uncle Tim?" she asked. "Did the nice man take it out?"

"He did," I said.

"Is that why you have a bandage?" she said. "Does it hurt?"

"It does hurt," I replied, "but it will get better."

It would get better. But first it would get a lot worse.

9

REFLECTIONS – THE PHYSICAL, THE MENTAL AND EVERYTHING IN BETWEEN

'd like to pause for a moment, before we continue the story. It's my firm belief that information is more valuable than gold, and if I'd known half of what I know now, the after-effects of my experience might have been easier to weather – and not just for me. And so, in this section, I would like to reach out to anyone in the same or similar situation to that which I found myself.

The most important thing to note is that research is key. The opportunity to recover as quickly as possible – following surgery – is one to be grasped. To achieve this, do not leave any stone unturned. Often health professionals will advise us not to Google too much, not to 'over-research' the problem. Of course, I needed to know what had been wrong with me, and understanding meningiomas was important. Cancer more generally – stats and stories, different treatment approaches – made for distressing reading. All information needs to be filtered carefully – it needs to be used for the good.

I've never smoked, so the advice not to wasn't difficult to follow, and I'd stopped drinking because of my medication. For me, the most important piece of advice related to diet and nutrition; doctors provided some advice on this, but it was left up to me to really delve down into the specifics of what that entailed. "Eat as healthily as possible" is a generic and arbitrary statement that doesn't especially help anyone.

So here's what I did. I substituted meat, by and large, for fish. I switched pasta and bacon butties for whatever came out of the ground – much more greenery. I wasn't working, so my business lunches – and often dinners, too – were curbed. Chocolate was now a monthly treat, rather than a twice-daily habit. I adopted a combination of keto and low-GI as my new diet: it was very important not to have too much sugar in the body. Aside from anything else, it's a natural cocaine, and makes the brain race. My brain needed the opposite of that.

What's fascinating to me is that one can be hospitalised during recovery: rehab is an option. But in a system based on budget, the food on offer is likely to make you gain weight and feel sluggish. There are limited resources when it comes to fresh, organic produce. And that's what the body really needs after a trauma. If you are able to, recover at home, and take control of what you're eating.

I was also low on vitamins – all types. I began to take

blood tests at home, which proved instrumental to charting my recovery. I requested a homocysteine blood test from my GP; the results showed I was especially low in vitamin B12, and needed 8,000 EC NRV a day to ensure my levels returned to normal. When I approached my GP to ask for the test, they had no idea what I was talking about. But the brain feeds off the workings of the body, after all, and there's a reason tumours are often called malignancies: mine had drawn all the goodness from me, and left me depleted. I downloaded an app to my phone which enabled me to track the changing levels of my blood, and soon enough – like a ski slope – I watched it zoom from 'abnormal' to 'normal'. It's proof, as though any were needed, that taking steps to monitor oneself does work.

My doctor once informed me that changing bad habits before the age of 60 was key, and I can see what he means. I'm fortunate enough to have levelled out my weight, I go running, I have made the alterations I needed to make in order to give myself the best possible chance of health going forward.

It's vital, too, to ensure a positive mental attitude: never "if" the surgery is a success, but "when". I know now that I've suffered from post-traumatic stress disorder, that there are certain memories and moments I do not want to revisit. And yet I refuse to be labelled – you have to dig deep, to refuse trauma a permanent place in your head, no pun intended. Through not working, and then changing the way in which I *did* work, I was able to give my body the rest it needed. I changed the way I thought about food, generally – it was no longer a diet, but a way of giving myself a better future. There are a whole host of reasons cancer may arrive in the body, but I'm sure that conflict within the self is at least partly to blame. There's a reason we call it a 'disease': if you're literally dis-eased within yourself, it's more likely to happen. My diagnosis dumped an enormous pile of bricks in front of me, and made me reconsider everything – now I just needed to put my new insights into practice at the right pace.

So how might my life have turned out differently, if all this hadn't happened? For starters, I'd probably be at least three stone heavier: I'm an excessive character and love the highs life can provide. I would still, no doubt, have been working in one marketing agency or another, ensuring I kept clients happy, keeping tabs on what came in and what went out. I've no idea what the future holds for me now, and the thought is a comforting one, whereas before it would have horrified me. I was given the opportunity to reset my life, to confront myself, to make positive changes.

But if I had to do it all again, I would make sure to maintain a greater dialogue with my friends. There were some, sadly, who were too frightened to speak to me about what I was going through, and over time both parties allowed the friendship to slip and slide. I got the sense, sometimes, that the standard "How are you?" question was one they didn't really want answered, in truth. But I suppose I would try harder to force dialogue on the subject, never to allow it to become an elephant in the room.

Later, as we will see, medication produced an adverse effect, and I underwent an organic but avoidable spell of mental ill health. It can be tricky to do so in the moment, but in hindsight, I should have investigated more, tried to understand what the medication was intended to do, and speak more openly with the consultants. I would advise anyone experiencing something similar to challenge, to ask questions, to ask for the full facts and potential consequences. And I'd make sure to verify where exactly my hospital notes would be, and when: having the medical history in the right place is vital, and the first two months of recovery generally could not be more crucial to longer-term prognoses.

It's easy to look back and admonish myself, though, so I refuse to. After the surgery we were all – myself, friends and family alike – exhausted. At that moment you're vulnerable, weak and confused. It is the doctors' responsibility to guide you through the next stages, of course: but if you're able to research what will be needed yourself, plan meals, commit to regular blood monitoring, take supplements, question medication and ensure a positive mental attitude, you stand a far greater chance of quicker recovery – both physical and emotional.

10

KASHMIR

What happened next was, I now know, a common consequence of major brain surgery. And due to the nature of the problem, I feel it prudent to reflect on Kashmir here: much of what followed is a blur to me, and perhaps it's better left that way. But without her, my recovery – both primary, following the surgery, and secondary, following a bad reaction to my medication – would have had a very different outcome altogether.

The double Olympic gold medallist James Cracknell underwent a similar surgery to mine. I can remember watching his videos, hearing him describe the process of recovery, and the shocking statistic that 80% of all people with brain injuries end up divorcing. In 2012, together with his wife Beverley Turner, James published *Touching Distance*, a book detailing the lives he and his family enjoyed both before and after the accident that changed his life forever. That cycling accident – and the frontal-lobe surgery required in the aftermath of his cerebral contusion – had left

Cracknell with epilepsy and a changed personality. Sadly, the couple did indeed part ways in 2019. I can't help but wonder how much can be attributed to the accident, the surgery and the consequences.

I'd started to become more active by around February 2019, and was regularly up and about. Going for a walk felt like the biggest, most exciting adventure. My physical state was improving, and so it stands to reason that I observed myself as on the mend, getting better every day. With Kashmir's help, I'd started investigating exactly what it was I needed to do to aid my recovery. She found a charity called Food For The Brain, for instance, who provided information on the best diet going forward, set cognitive-function tests, and recommended things I could do for myself to speed up the process of recovery. An occupational therapist continued to visit me at home, something that continued up until July of that year. In the early part of May, I attended one of Food For The Brain's seminars – a truly life-changing event – and was able to meet professors and doctors who understood how food affects the body and brain. I felt inspired, full of energy and motivation, and it was around this time that I decided what I needed was a trip to New York.

For the past months I'd been increasingly difficult to live with; I can see that in hindsight. Kashmir and I were arguing and I'd no idea why. I couldn't see the changes in myself. When I announced that I wanted to fly to the States, she didn't know what to do, but felt that if this was what I needed, so be it. I wanted, ostensibly, to attend an art exhibition in the city – that was the trip's main purpose. I also felt it would be wise to give myself some space.

It wasn't a good idea.

I felt terrible in New York: emotional about the state of my marriage, and I stopped taking the Keppra – epilepsy medication I'd been prescribed on leaving hospital. S, I, so, lwent to the airport, The trip was scheduled to last five days, but I had come home after three. Later down the line I'd be informed that brain surgery can bring about a form of organic psychosis: part of the reason I'd been put on so many different drugs after the operation. They were intended to make me better, but I reacted badly to them.

Kashmir arrived and drove me straight to St George's. I was admitted on 22nd May and remained there until the 29th, monitored and receiving intravenous drugs to make up for the loss of medication in New York. I badly needed stabilising, not only due to the withdrawal but the jetlag too, and was talking utter gibberish. I was placed under the hospital's psychiatric care, and was placed on a different epilepsy drug called Oxcarbazepine as well as Risperidone (often administered to patients suffering from schizophrenia). Yet again another drug interaction, another intervention that seemed to worsen my symptoms after discharge. By this point, Kashmir and I were suffering badly – it was like my whole personality had changed. A classic Libran, I'd been calm and considered beforehand: reflective, not prone to bouts of anger or temper. And now I'd flare up with little warning, become angry, start arguments – once in front of the hospital psychiatrist in July.

I moved out. For the next two weeks I lived in my father's one-bedroom home, and felt that life was truly falling apart. The problem was, I had none of the tools to fix it. I announced we needed a divorce, Kashmir and I, and checked myself into a hotel. That night I had a bad allergic reaction to some food I'd ordered, and became disruptive; the hotel staff decided to call the police, who recommended I be taken to hospital immediately.

And so it was, in June 2019, that I found myself sectioned under the Mental Health Act in St Thomas', a general hospital with no specialist knowledge of what was happening to me. It was just after midnight when I was interviewed by two psychiatrists who promptly referred me to a mental-health facility in Highgate. I needed to be with the team at St George's, the team who understood my history and my needs, but I went to the wrong place.

I was discharged from the facility and the section after just four days – I only stayed for one night in the Highgate facility – but I still suffered from another appalling bout of psychosis. Later, I'd be informed that the action taken by the admittance team at St Thomas' had been inappropriate – but in my current state I'd had no way of knowing this or expressing myself.

I wouldn't wish psychosis on my worst enemy. But the

time spent at the facility in Highgate was by far the worst experience of this whole ordeal: it was such a frightening environment. I felt like I was trapped and possessed – that's the only way of accurately describing it. I was doing and saying things that were totally out of character. Thankfully, Kashmir was there to rescue me. The trip to New York was pointless: there was no real reason for me to go. But when someone presents as physically well on the outside, it can be all too easy to imagine that nothing is wrong, that they're indulging in some bizarre fantasy without any sort of mental-health issue. Kashmir could see I wasn't myself, but since we had no idea that the kind of surgery I had undergone could precipitate a period of psychosis – a whole personality-change – neither of us was able to join the dots.

We'd spoken, Kashmir and I, every few days while I was living outside the family home. She was able to explain to the team at Highgate that I needed to be referred back to St George's, and after various meetings with consultants there, my medication was changed in August 2019. Now I was on Olanzapine, an anti-psychotic, which more than anything else proved the saving grace. I calmed down completely, took the medication at night and slept.

It was a torrid time, and – following the trauma and anxiety of my diagnosis and the operation itself – a terrible burden on my wife. For the awful months spent taking the initial medication I'd barely slept at night and disturbed the household simply by being awake at the most bizarre hours. I was argumentative, rude, difficult: a totally different person to the man she had married just five short years before.

I want to thank her. Not many people could or would have stuck with our relationship: so little is understood about complex mental-health issues following surgery, and it would be all too easy to cling to past wrongs, to ruminate on what I did wrong and prevent us from moving forward. Kashmir was there from the moment I fell ill, and the only times she couldn't be happened when I actively pushed her away. It's frightening to consider just how all-encompassing these drugs can be. I'd made the person I loved the most resist being around me. It was none of it my fault, but the fact remains I'm a lucky man. Not everyone would be afforded a second chance. Psychosis is a terrifying thing to witness in one's partner.

By mid-November of 2019, however, I had returned to our home. We bought a new house and began renovations: and then the lockdown hit. For so many, the past year has been desperate: I'm very fortunate to say that for us, for Kashmir and me, it's been a blessing. We've forged our relationship into a stronger state than it was even before all this horror began; we've taken the time to rediscover one another, to love well, to watch our 'forever home' coming together before our eyes. Before Covid, and before my health problems, we had been fine, but coasting. The past few years has shown us both, I think, that we can now thrive in our marriage rather than simply exist. It's a new chapter, a new phase. We have learned, quite simply, to love each other better. And who could ask for more? The support, the kindness, the worry and fear she endured, the hospital appointments, the experience of watching someone you knew transform beyond all recognition – she dealt with it all, carried it in her stride, refused to give up on us. She's the love of my life, this woman, and I couldn't be more thankful for her.

Happy future together.

11

BACK TO THE FUTURE

There are moments, though they're mercifully less and less common, when I still can't quite believe what happened to me. I think about the tumult of it all, the ups and downs, the rollercoaster of emotions, the relief, the pain, the suffering, the complete mental collapse. These are the things the doctors cannot prepare one for: their job, quite rightly, is to mend the body. And they mended mine. But afterwards came, as Mr Stapleton had predicted, the long road to recovery.

We take our bodies for granted, don't we? One moment we're up on our feet, playing tracks at a party, enjoying golf with friends, talking and eating and full of animation. We don't think about the background hum of the heart, the lungs, the liver and kidneys and the brain that controls it all. Before a health problem occurs, one could be forgiven for not paying the slightest bit of attention to the body – it simply works, it does its job, it functions. And suddenly, one day, it betrays us. We fall, we stumble, we slur our speech and vomit and can't remember how we came to be under the harsh, clinical lighting of an A&E admissions ward.

I'm in good physical shape now, but 2019 – and all that happened after the operation – certainly produced a post-traumatic response. There were so many moments of tension and fear: when my glasses were smashed during the initial collapse, I found myself worried sick over an optician's appointment to order some new ones. At any moment, I felt, the optometrist would inform me that my eyes had been damaged beyond repair during the surgery, that some terrible scarring had taken place that could never be rectified. He was a kind man, and made sure to check my eyes incredibly carefully – his reassurance meant the world to me, but soon enough I was tormented by another physical sensation. I'd have these incredibly strong sensations in my head, right in the spot the surgeons had cut, and they caused me no end of anxiety. I had an incessant urge to scratch at the scar. At my next consultation with Mr Stapleton, I was informed that my nerve endings were simply reattaching following the procedure. Not knowing this in advance meant I hadn't been prepared for it, hadn't felt able to touch the back of my head at all. I wrapped myself in cotton wool, because when I'd failed to do so before – living my normal life in October 2018 – look what had happened.

I've been patient with myself, and these moments of fear are gradually subsiding now. I have a small dent, a depression at the side of my head, and every day it reminds me that I'm lucky to be alive. We all experience positive and negative moments every day – it's so important to focus on the positive, to trust that the operation was a success and believe that to be a firm fact. I could have been damaged beyond all repair by my illness, but I wasn't. My brain might never have recovered – it did. I am in good shape and I need to keep reminding myself of that.

I had no information on what might happen to me after surgery, besides the physical. One change I might recommend to the NHS protocol is instruction on various outcomes, following new medication. If Kashmir had been told to watch out for irrational behaviour, for last-minute trips to New York, for irritability and indeed a complete change of personality, we might have fared better. There was not enough support where immediate mental recovery was concerned. And it didn't help that my discharge necessitated a change in care – St George's fell under the umbrella of Merton council, but on leaving hospital I was remanded to the care of the borough of Camden. My files needed to be transferred, a process that took two months, and thus I fell through the cracks.

I have realised that two competing things can be absolutely true at the same time. The NHS saved my life: they removed the tumour and made me well again. They cared for me, reassured me, made me laugh, brought me food, held my hand, comforted me. At the same time, my issues with the prescribed medication could have been avoided. That lack of post-operative psychological support could have cost me my marriage.

I don't regret what happened to me, nor do I believe in self-pity, or questions like "Why me?" After all, why not me? Worse things could have happened and they didn't. I'm one of the lucky ones: my tumour wasn't cancerous, my surgery was a success, and I'm now well on the road to a full recovery. My medication needed some refinement, to put it lightly, but as complications go things could have been much more dire.

And the experience has taught me so much: about patience and kindness, about tolerance. The hours spent redecorating our house have been so calm, so quietly peaceful. We've made the garden look presentable, become more friendly with our neighbours, and taken the time to recover from this shared experience. Kashmir and I have been together for 12 years, but it's really over the past 12 months that we've found a new, deeper closeness neither of us foresaw. She tells me I am now the man she met and fell in love with all those years ago, only better.

Our lives before the meningioma were fast-paced, frenetic. We'd go out to restaurants, of course, and spend time together, but the lockdown has meant we now spend our evenings really engaging, watching Netflix series together under a duvet, blocking the world out.

I have four years remaining under the review of Mr Stapleton, but these check-ups are once a year now, and for any other health concerns my first port of call is my own GP. I made such progress on my new medication that I was taken off the anti-psychosis drugs last June, and was discharged formally in February this year. It feels normal, dare I say it: there is so little intervention, now. It makes a welcome change.

I can't apologise for the way the initial medication made me behave: it wasn't my fault. But I can and do apologise for the pain it brought to family and friends, and particularly Kashmir. I've since undergone counselling through the NHS and also privately, as has my wife. I went to see a psychiatrist at a charity called Headway, which caters for those with mental-health and brain-recovery problems, but unfortunately the experience brought up many memories which I'd dealt with previously, and didn't need tinkering with. Nonetheless, we really believe in the value of talking things through, of seeking outside help to improve one's life and relationships.

Psychosis marked the lowest point of my journey, but it also taught me valuable lessons. How lucky we are, I think now, to feel in control of ourselves, of our thoughts and emotions and beliefs. I was able to respect others, afterwards, in a way I might have struggled to before. I wasn't listening when I was ill, and the aftermath of a mental breakdown such as the one I suffered necessitates a re-evaluation of others' thoughts and opinions. I needed to hear what Kashmir had to say, what my friends and family were trying to tell me. I retrained my brain. And yet, at any point, I could have given up, and been lost forever. I never once had a suicidal thought, throughout my worst days, but I did feel – particularly in New York, when I was so alone and so unwell – that anything might have happened to me. In hindsight, I can now unpack these 'what if?' thoughts and accept that I got through it. We can't go back in time, and what happened happened: there's little point worrying about the past.

Some days are better than others – of course they are. I find it difficult, on occasion, to pull myself out of thoughts and reflections of the ordeal. Sometimes the drama and the trauma of it all rears its head. I recount the story on Monday and I feel fine; by Tuesday I find the whole experience of retelling emotionally charged. It's a constant process of readjustment, of getting one's head – no pun intended – around what happened, especially since it's all so recent.

To anyone reading this and preparing to undergo something similar: all I can say is have faith. Believe in yourself. The human body has the ability to heal – we all break bones, we slip, we fall. You just have to get up again and focus on the next step, the next minute, hour and day. Illnesses can be fatal, tumours malignant. It's a set of circumstances one cannot predict or prevent from happening, just as we might step out into the road at the wrong time one day. But accept that these sorts of health problems cannot be ignored. They must be dealt with. Ask questions of your medical team – don't take anything for granted. Research what you feel you can. Be disruptive with a doctor if you don't understand. Ask the questions.

Looking to the future, I'm excited about the prospect of returning to full-time employment, to restarting my career and returning to industry, business and commerce. I've missed the pace, the routine and structure provided by full-time work, by putting skills to use. This will be so important for continued emotional stability, and for my all-important sense of purpose. And I hope – with full expectation of success – to have a long and happy marriage. My wants are simple, now, my desires simply derived from enjoying one day to the next: watching sunrises and sunsets and feeling blessed to be here. It's almost spring now, and the weather is changing: the trees begin to blossom and the mornings are warm, full of promise. Long may it continue. My final words are the ones that carried me through all of this: onwards and upwards!

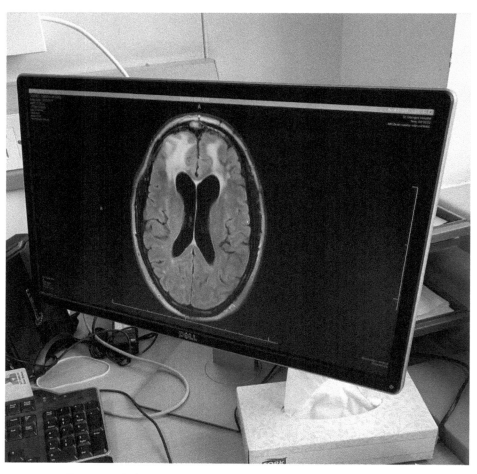

Post surgery MRI. Just showing some fluid which has now gone and no tumour!

The surviver!

Lightning Source UK Ltd.
Milton Keynes UK
UKHW021134090322
399755UK00006B/317